Keep Well Day

by **Meish Goldish**
illustrated by **Nancy Davis**

Orlando   Boston   Dallas   Chicago   San Diego

Visit *The Learning Site!*
www.harcourtschool.com

At South County School,
doctors from all around town
came to Keep Well Day. Wow!
What a crowd!

2

The doctors met all of the students. They checked to see that they took good care of their bodies. How busy the doctors were!

Dr. Carr is an ear doctor. He found out how well the students can hear. He used a machine that makes low and high sounds.

"Can you hear the low
sounds?" Dr. Carr asked. "How
about the high sounds?" He
wrote what each student said.

Dr. Chow is an eye doctor. She found out how well the students see. They read a chart with rows of big and small letters.

6

"Call out the letters in the top row," Dr. Chow said. "How about the next row? How about the row after that?"

Dr. Brown is a dentist. He
checked each student's teeth.
"Open your mouth wide,"
he said. He looked all around
each mouth.

8

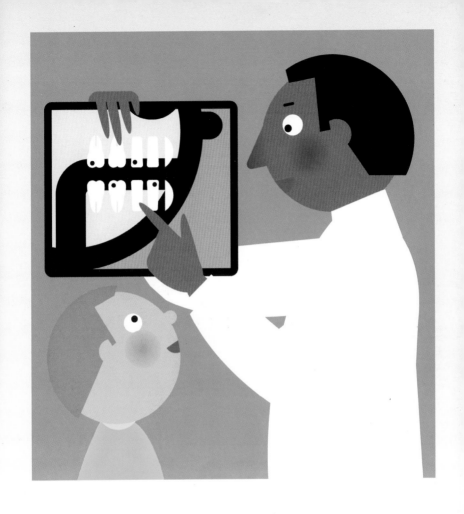

Dr. Brown found eight
cavities in one mouth. How
about that! "Keep candy out of
your house!" Dr. Brown said.

Dr. Powers is a family doctor. She found out how healthy the students were. First she checked how much they weighed.

Then Dr. Powers listened to the sounds of their hearts. She counted the number of beats. She took down the amount.

The doctors' tests were over. Then they spoke to the crowd. They told the students how to take care of their bodies.

"Do not stick any small objects in your ears," said Dr. Carr. "Wash the dirt out every day. Keep your ears very clean."

13

"If you can't see well, tell someone about it," said Dr. Chow. "Don't play around with your eyes."

"Brush your teeth in circles,"
said Dr. Brown. "Brush for
about three minutes
after every meal."

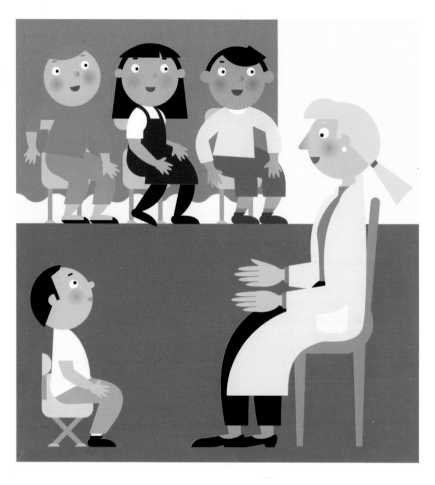

"Sit up, don't slouch," said
Dr. Powers. "Run around to
exercise. Eat the right amount
of good foods. Keep well and
be proud!"